play guitar with...

velvet revol[

fall out boy, linkin par[
foo fighters, wolfmother,
smashing pumpkins, biffy clyro
and queens of the stone age

Wise Publications
part of The Music Sales Group
London / New York / Paris / Sydney / Copenhagen / Berlin / Madrid / Tokyo

joker & the thief

Words & Music by
Andrew Stockdale, Chris Ross & Myles Heskett

Full performance demo: CD track 1
Backing only: CD track 9

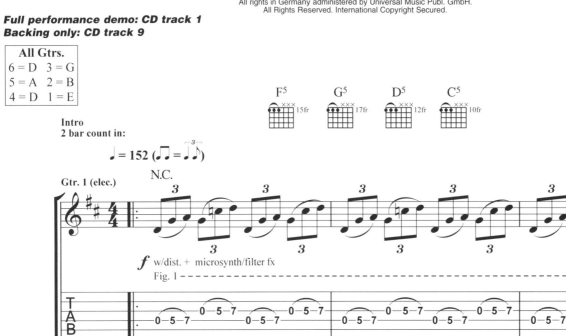

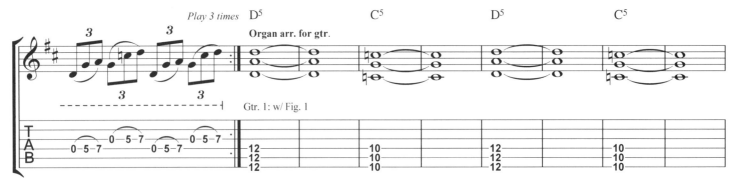

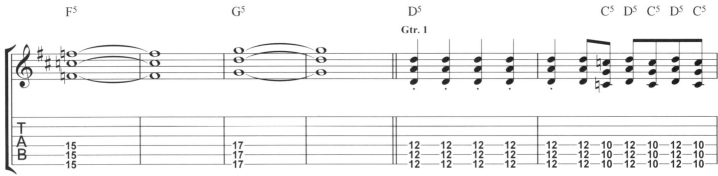

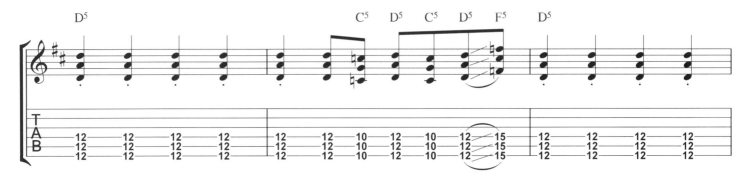

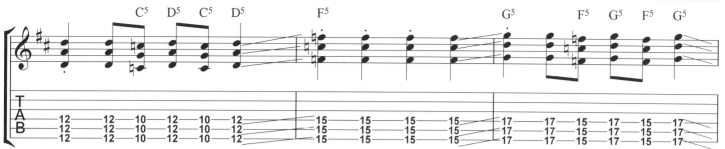

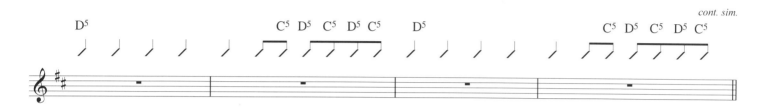

Verse

1. I said the Jok - er is a want - ed man.___ He makes his way all a -
3. What you see,___ well, you might not know.___ You get the feel in' com - in'

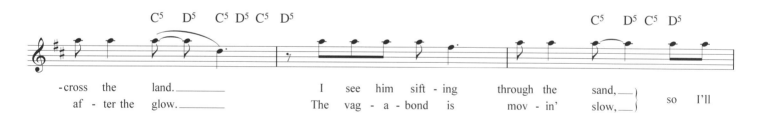

-cross the land._____ I see him sift - ing through the sand,___ } so I'll
af - ter the glow._____ The vag - a - bond is mov - in' slow,___ }

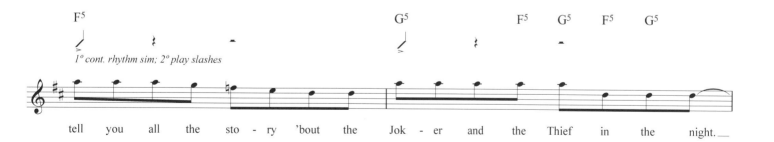

1° cont. rhythm sim; 2° play slashes

tell you all the sto - ry 'bout the Jok - er and the Thief in the night.___

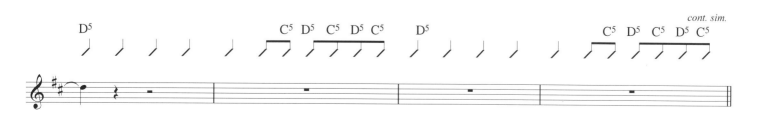

Verse

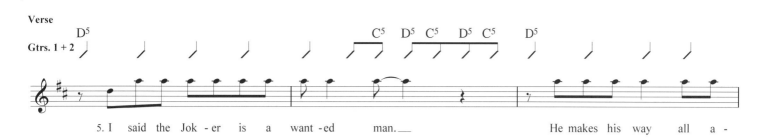

5. I said the Jok - er is a want -ed man.___ He makes his way all a -

-cross the land._____ I see him sift - ing through the sand,__ so I'll

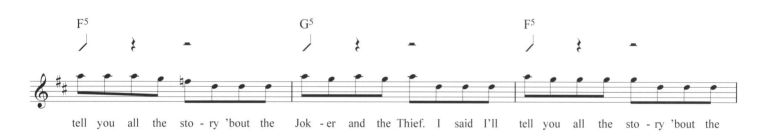

tell you all the sto - ry 'bout the Jok - er and the Thief. I said I'll tell you all the sto - ry 'bout the

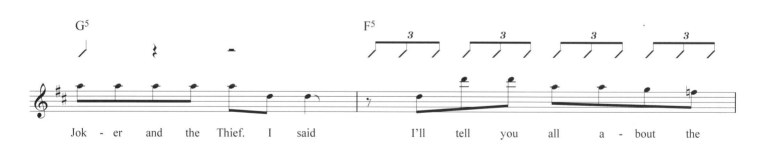

Jok - er and the Thief. I said I'll tell you all a - bout the

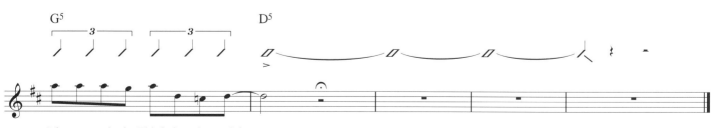

Jok - er and the Thief in the night.___

the pretender

Words & Music by
Dave Grohl, Taylor Hawkins, Nate Mendel & Chris Shiflett

Full performance demo: CD track 2
Backing only: CD track 10

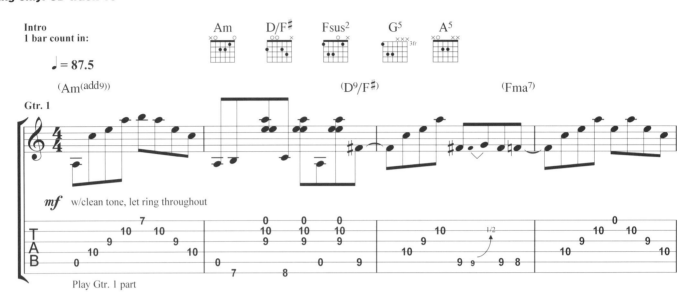

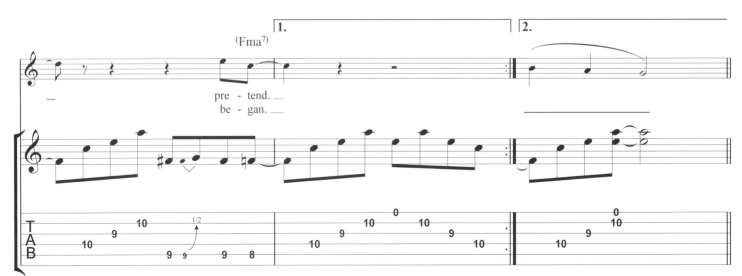

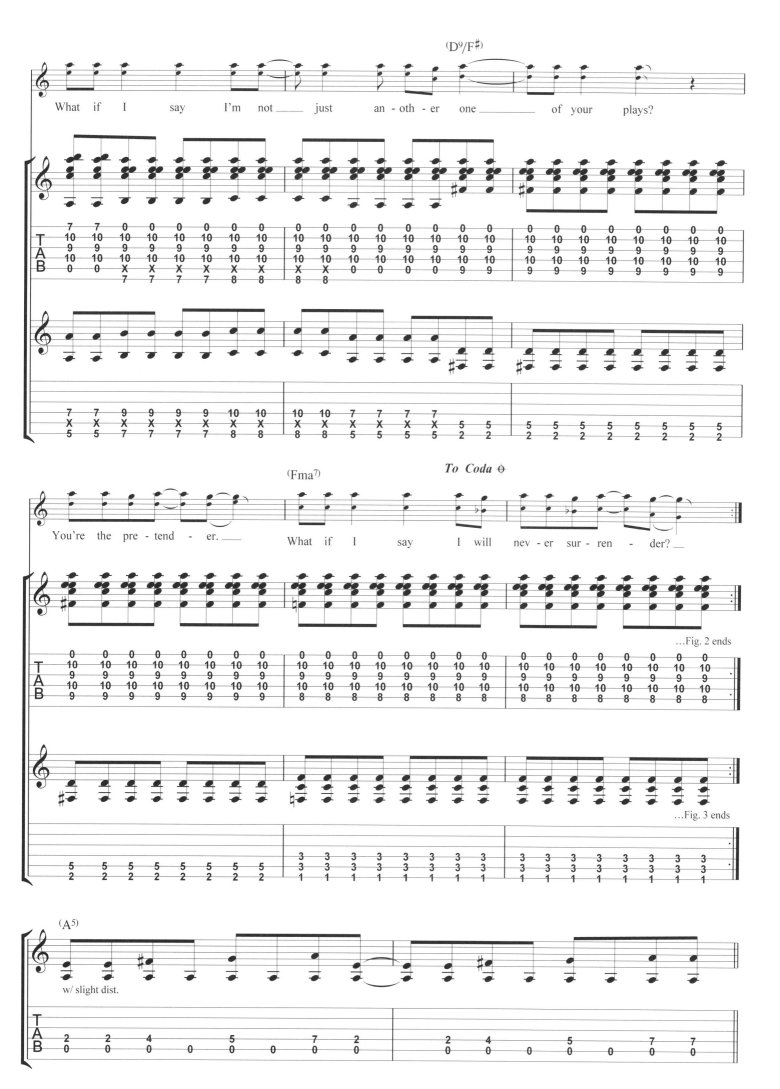

⊕ *Coda*

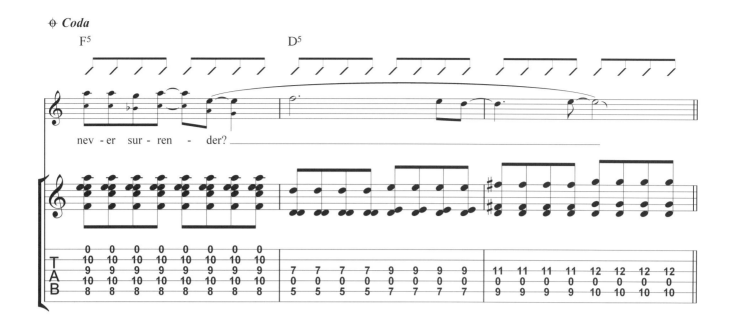

nev - er - sur - ren - der? _____

Interlude

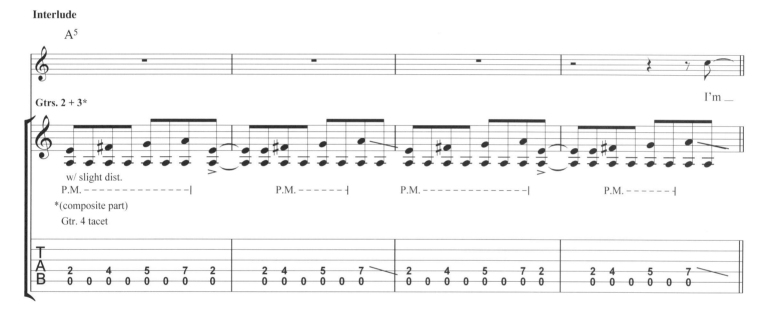

I'm __

Gtrs. 2 + 3*

w/ slight dist.
*(composite part)
Gtr. 4 tacet

Bridge

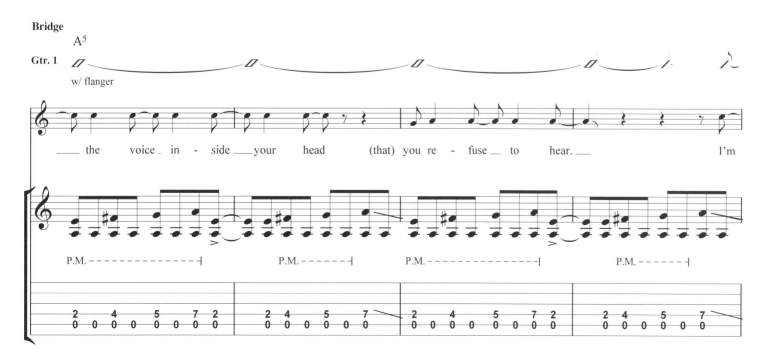

Gtr. 1

w/ flanger

___ the   voice _ in - side ___ your   head   (that) you re - fuse ___ to   hear. ___   I'm

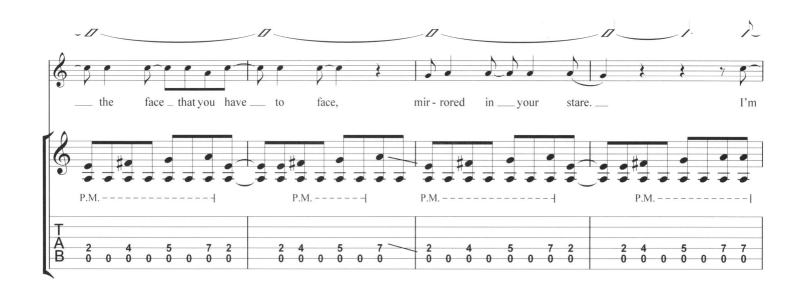

the face that you have to face, mir - rored in your stare. I'm

Add **Gtr. 4** in ♪'s (A5)

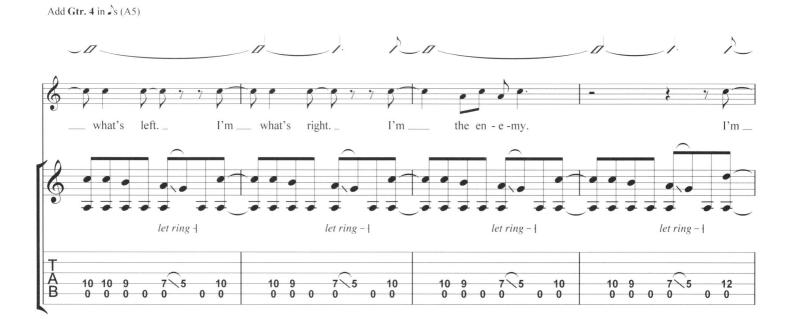

what's left. I'm what's right. I'm the en - e - my. I'm

A5

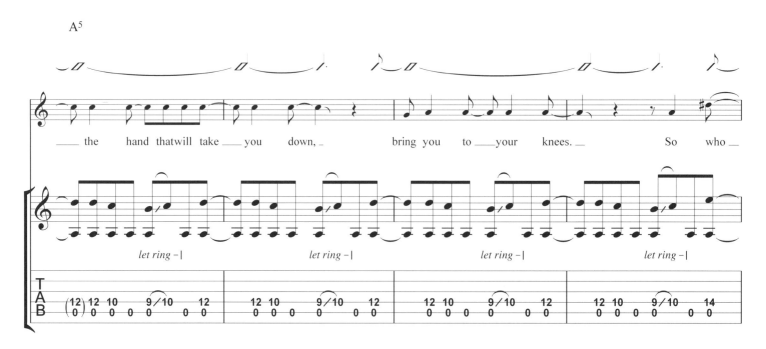

the hand that will take you down, bring you to your knees. So who

Double tempo ♩ = 175

Chorus

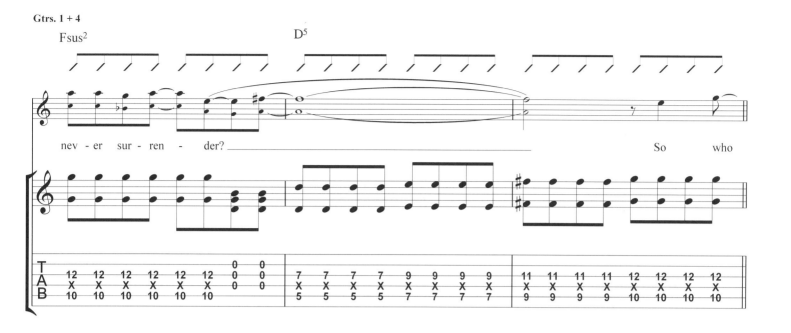

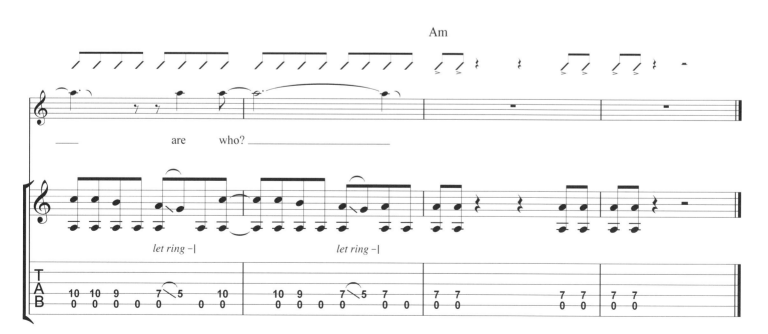

saturday superhouse

Words & Music by Simon Neil

Full performance demo: CD track 3
Backing only: CD track 11

1. I'll___ be sit-ting on the left___
2. There's a do-zen corp-ses on the left___

side,___ you'll___ be sit-ting on the right.___ Dying___
side,___ I swear___ one's smi-ling at me.___ Com -

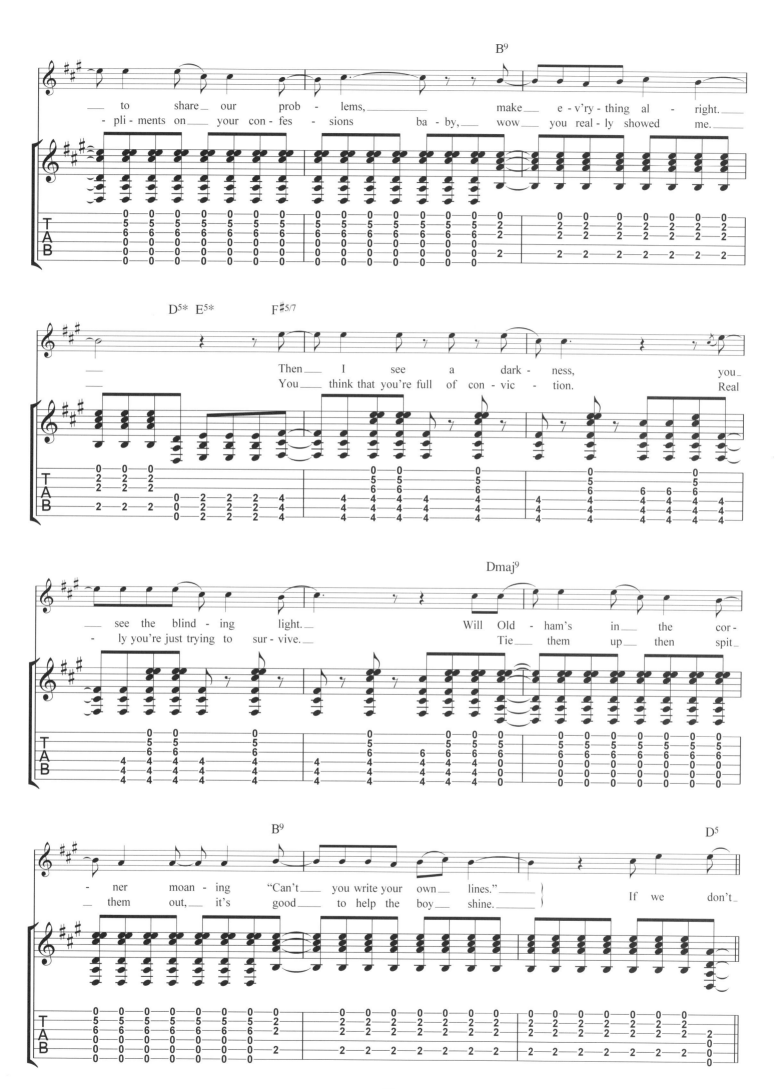

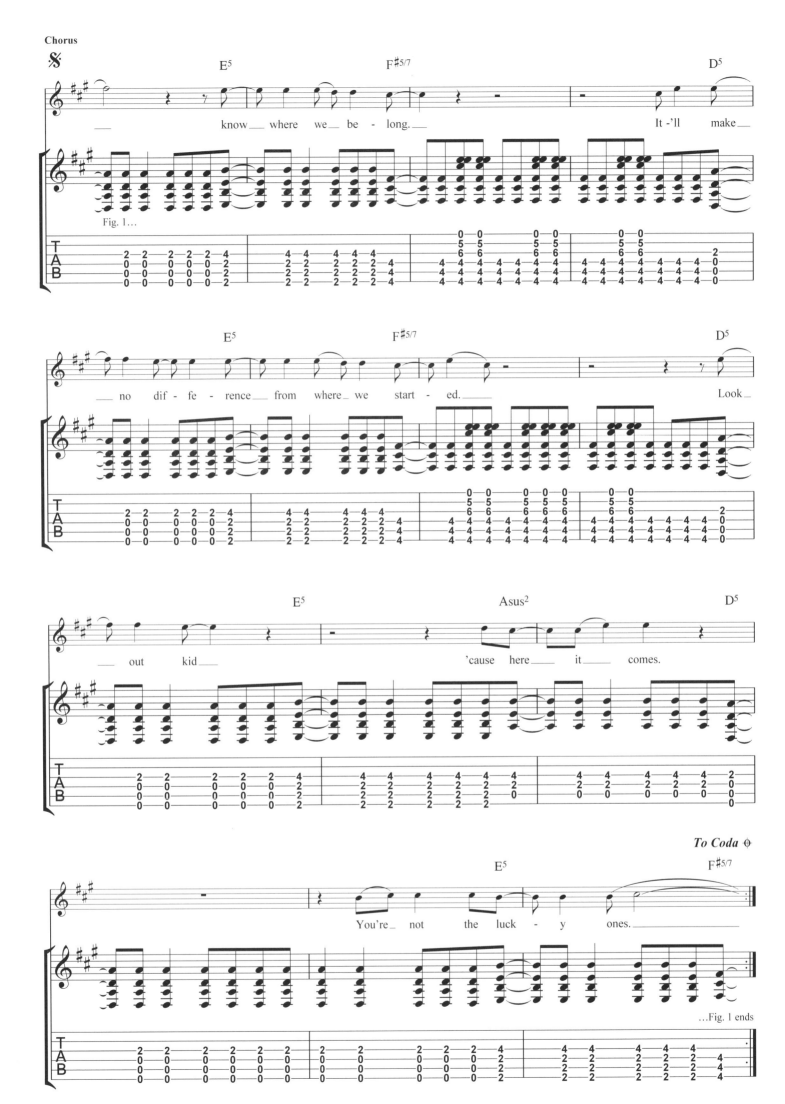

Coda

Chorus

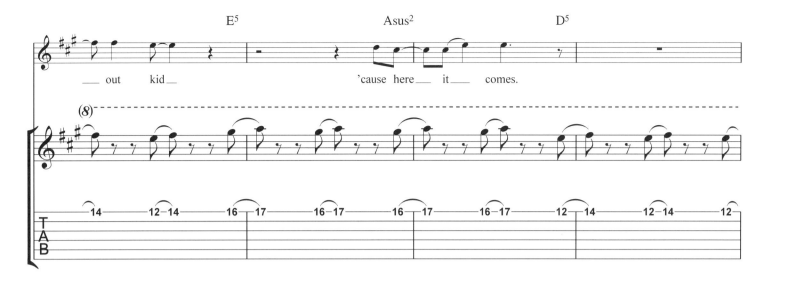

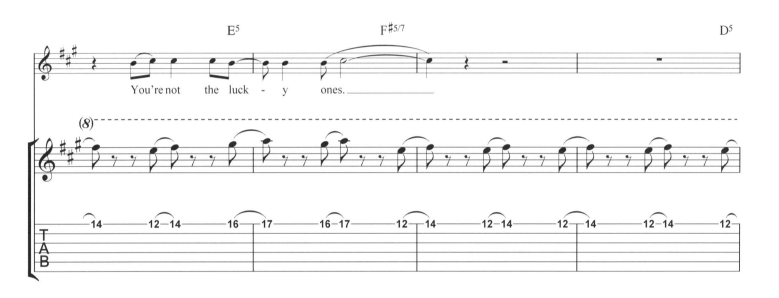

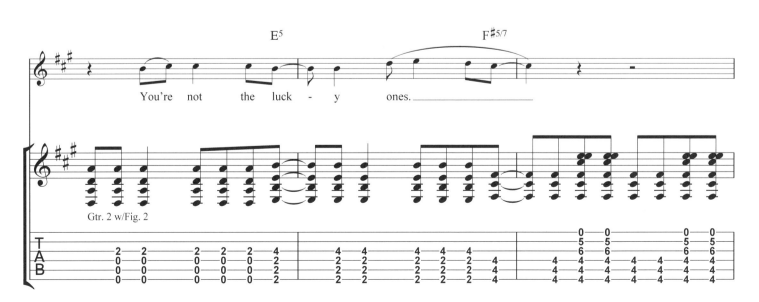

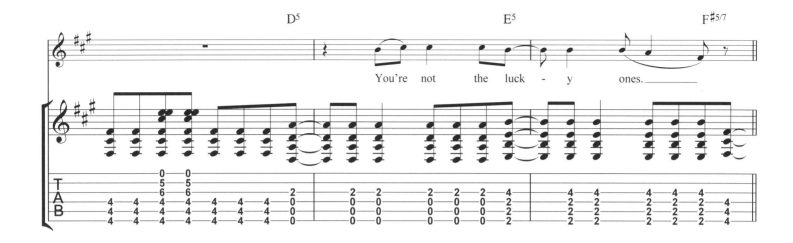

You're not the luck - y ones. _____

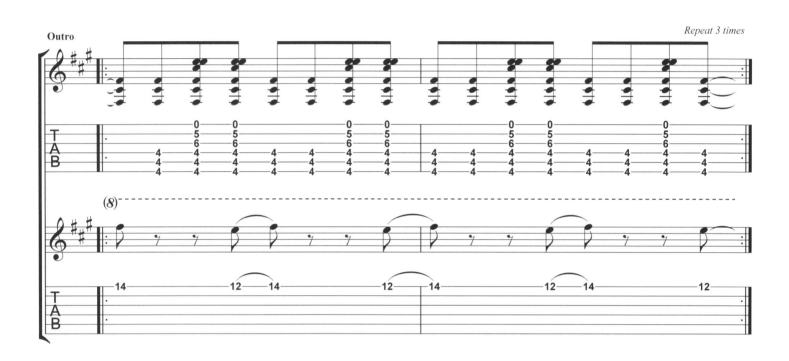

Outro

Repeat 3 times

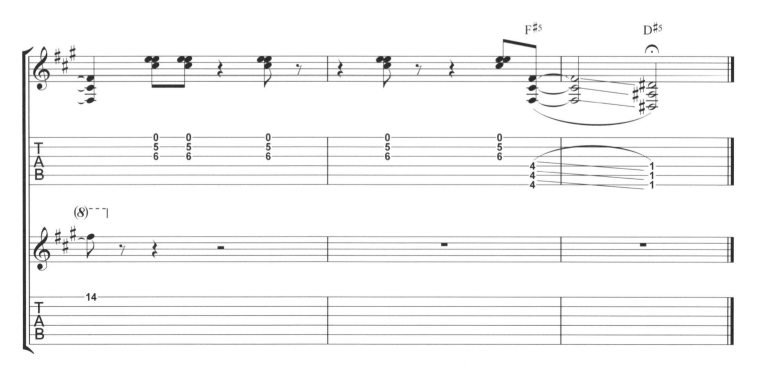

tarantula

Words & Music by Billy Corgan

Full performance demo: CD track 4
Backing only: CD track 12

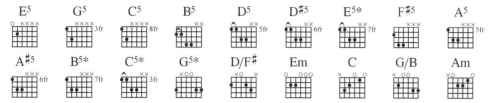

To match recording tune all strings down a semitone

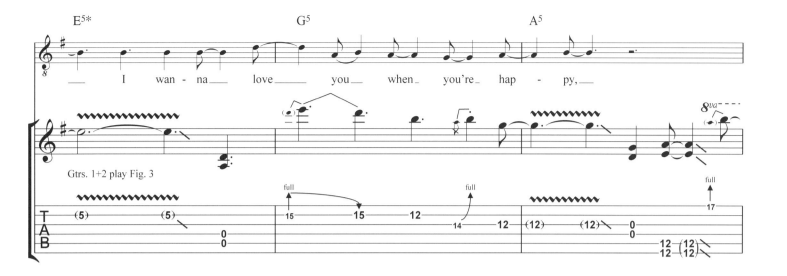

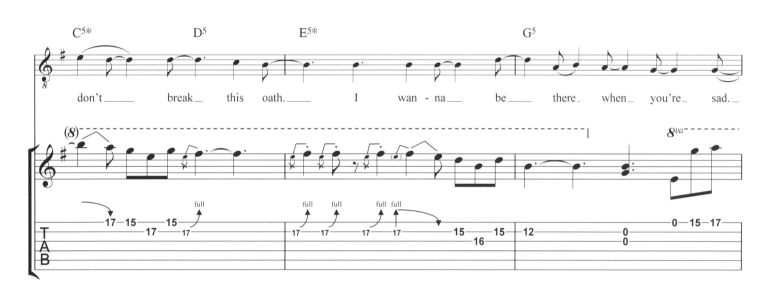

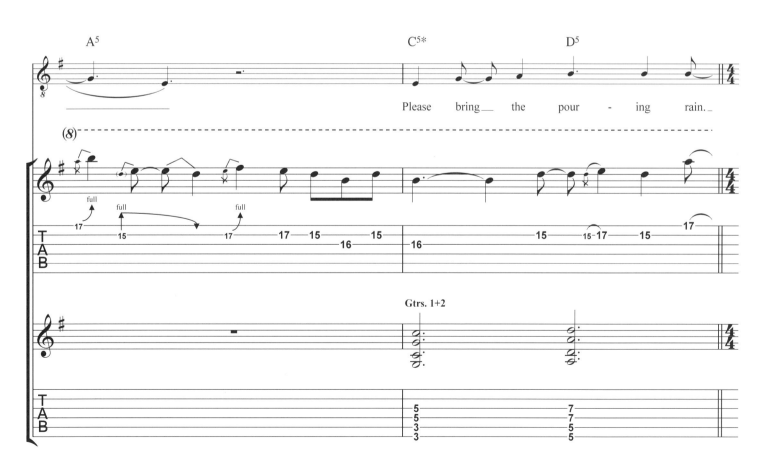

all are real, as real as an - y laws,

(let ring)

so ea - sy now. We all are real __ in ev -'ry liv - ing soul.

add **Gtrs. 1+2**

A young day, _____ you know.

Gtr. 3

32

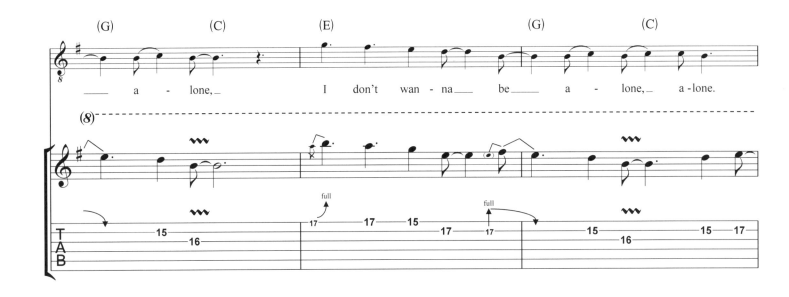

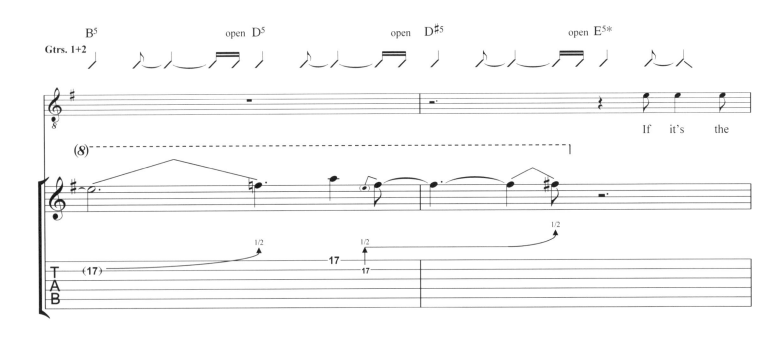

34

the black hot___ they'll get.

she builds quick machines

Words & Music by
Slash, Matt Sorum, Duff 'Rose' McKagan, Scott Weiland & David Kushner

Full performance demo: CD track 5
Backing only: CD track 13

Eyes___ cold as the snow. She___ built a quick dream.
Old ex in Veg - as don't back Tex - as.___

Gtr. 1 w/Fig. 2   Fig. 3

Play Gtr. 1 part

Gtr. 1 w/Fig. 2
Gtr. 2 w/Fig. 3

Sis - ter keep her mo -tor clean. Sol - id vi -sions and a wet ma -chine.
She burned through in -her -it -ance,___ dashed a -cross A -mer -i - ca.

She's al -ways quick to fight. We'll break her through to - night.___
At the all night sex show, so far from home.___

Let ring w/vib.

Pre-chorus

Half-time feel

End half-time feel

Chorus

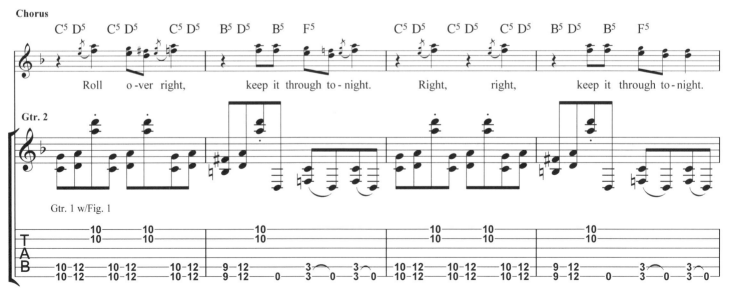

3's & 7's

Words & Music by
Josh Homme, Joey Castillo & Troy Van Leeuwen

Full performance demo: CD track 6
Backing only: CD track 14

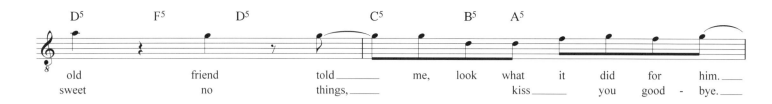

old   friend   told_____   me,   look what it did for him.

sweet   no   things,_____   kiss_____ you good - bye.

Whoah,_____   whoah._____

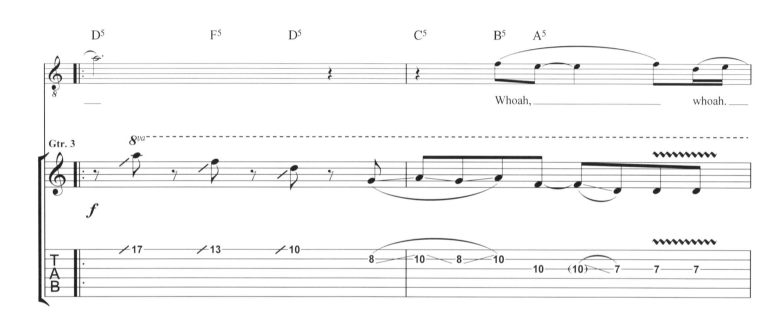

Whoah,_____   whoah.

Gtr. 3   *8va*

f

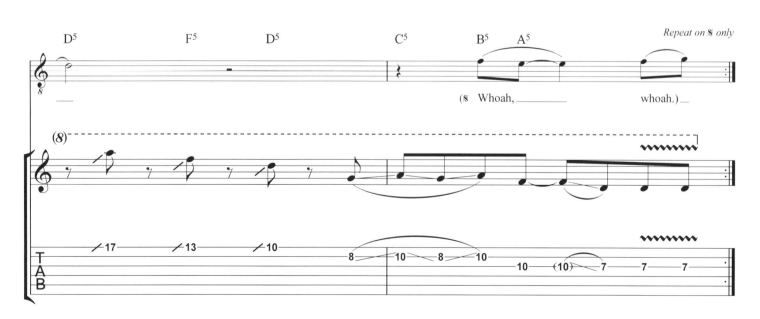

Repeat on ℅ only

(℅ Whoah,_____   whoah.)__

(8)

this ain't a scene, it's an arms race

Words & Music by
Peter Wentz, Andrew Hurley, Joseph Trohman & Patrick Stumph

Full performance demo: CD track 7
Backing only: CD track 15

Play Gtr. 1 part

Pre-Chorus

I'm not a shoul-der to cry on.____ but I____ di - gress.
Band-wag-on's full____ please, catch an - oth - er.

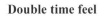

Double time feel

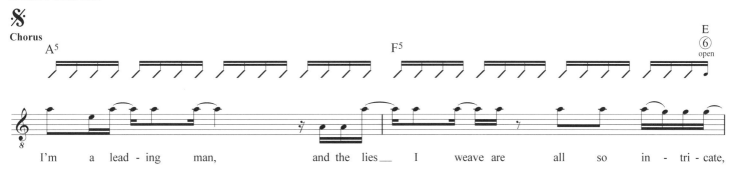

I'm a lead-ing man, and the lies____ I weave are all so in - tri-cate,

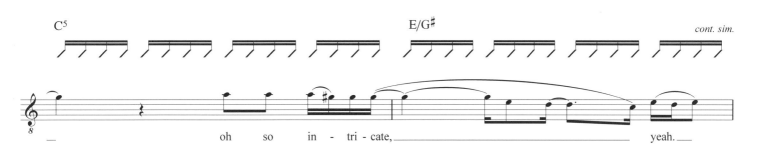

____ oh so in - tri-cate,_____ yeah.

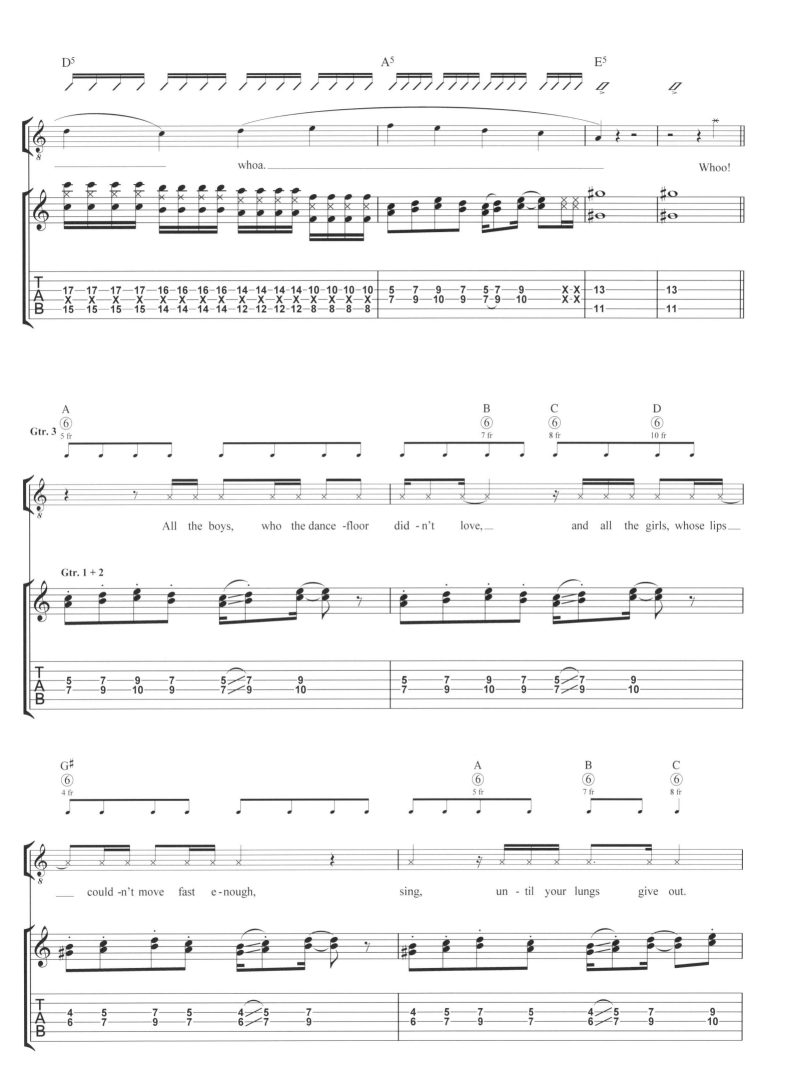

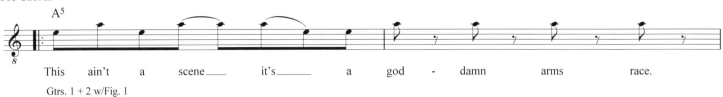

This ain't a scene___ it's___ a god - damn arms race.

Gtrs. 1 + 2 w/Fig. 1

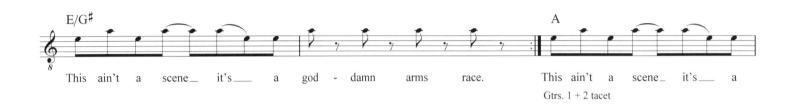

This ain't a scene__ it's__ a god - damn arms race. This ain't a scene__ it's__ a

Gtrs. 1 + 2 tacet

D.S. al Coda

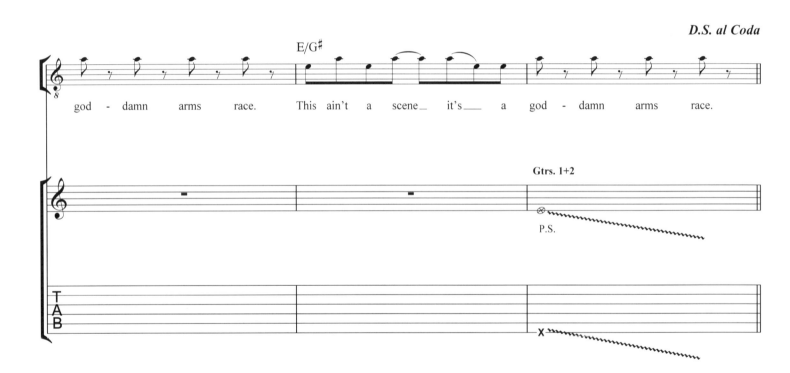

god - damn arms race. This ain't a scene__ it's__ a god - damn arms race.

Gtrs. 1+2

P.S.

Coda

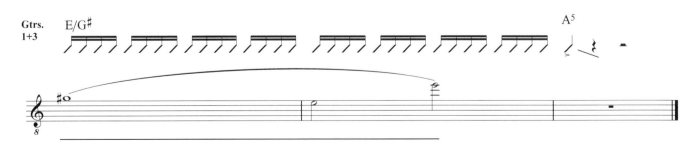

Gtrs.
1+3

what i've done

Words & Music by

Chester Bennington, Mike Shinoda, Rob Bourdon, Joseph Hahn, Brad Delson & Dave Farrell

Full performance demo: CD track 8
Backing only: CD track 16

Play Gtr. 1 part

Verse

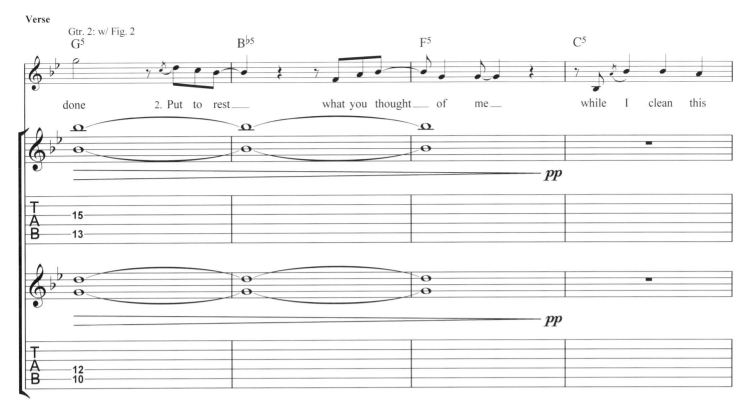

done   2. Put to rest___   what you thought___ of   me___   while   I   clean   this

slate   with the hands___   of un-cer - tain - ty.___   So   let   mer - cy

Coda

Half-time feel

Guitar Solo
Gtr. 1 w/Fig. 1
Gtr. 2 w/Fig. 2

what___   I've   done.___

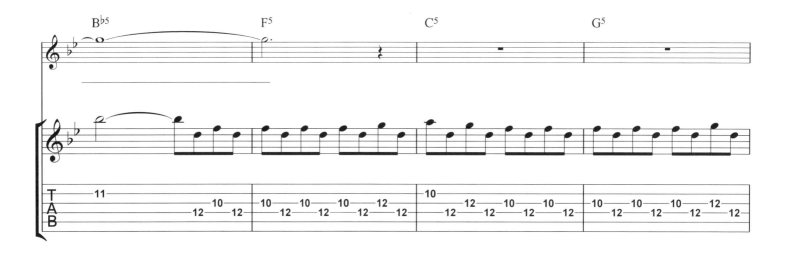

Gtr. 1: w/Fig. 3
Gtr. 2: w/Fig. 4

End half-time feel

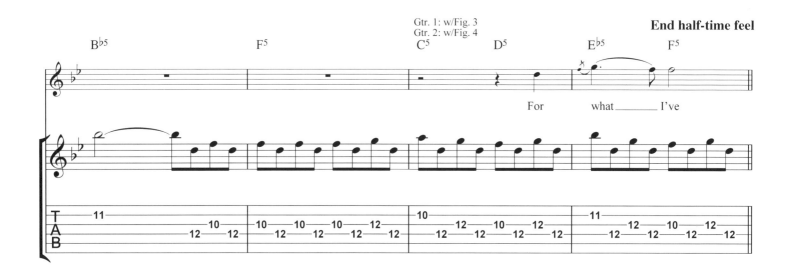

For what _____ I've

Bridge

done.   I   start   a - gain   and   what - ev - er   pain _____ may

CD track listing

Full instrumental performances (with guitar)...

1 joker and the thief
(Stockdale/Ross/Heskett)
Universal Music Publishing Limited.

2 the pretender
(Grohl/Hawkins/Mendel/Shiflett)
Universal Music Publishing Limited
/Bug Music Limited.

3 saturday superhouse
(Neil)
Universal Music Publishing Limited.

4 tarantula
(Corgan)
Universal Music Publishing Limited.

5 she builds quick machines
(Sorum/McKagan/Weiland/Kushner/Slash)
Chrysalis Music Limited/
Warner/Chappell Artemis Music Limited.

6 3's & 7's
(Homme/Castillo/Van Leeuwen)
Universal Music Publishing Limited.

**7 this ain't a scene,
it's an arms race**
(Wentz/Hurley/Trohman/Stumph)
Sony/ATV Music Publishing (UK) Limited.

8 what i've done
(Bennington/Shinoda/Bourdon/Hahn/Delson/Farrell)
Zomba Music Publishers Limited.

Backing tracks only (without guitar)...

9 joker and the thief
10 the pretender
11 saturday superhouse
12 tarantula
13 she builds quick machines
14 3's & 7's
**15 this ain't a scene,
it's an arms race**
16 what i've done

> To remove your CD from the plastic sleeve, lift the small lip on the side to break the perforated flap. Replace the disc after use for convenient storage.

Published by

Wise Publications
14-15 Berners Street, London W1T 3LJ, UK

Exclusive Distributors:

Music Sales Limited
Distribution Centre, Newmarket Road,
Bury St Edmunds, Suffolk IP33 3YB, UK

Music Sales Pty Limited
120 Rothschild Avenue,
Rosebery, NSW 2018, Australia

Order No. AM992068
ISBN 978-1-84772-308-6
This book © Copyright 2008 Wise Publications,
a division of Music Sales Limited.

www.musicsales.com

Compiled by Nick Crispin
Music arranged by Arthur Dick
Edited by Tom Farncombe
Music processed by Paul Ewers Music Design

All Guitars by Arthur Dick
Drums by Brett Morgan
Bass by Tom Farncombe

CD recorded, mixed and mastered by Jonas Persson

Your Guarantee of Quality
*As publishers, we strive to produce every book
to the highest commercial standards.
The music has been freshly engraved and the book has
been carefully designed to minimise awkward page turns
and to make playing from it a real pleasure.
Particular care has been given to specifying acid-free,
neutral-sized paper made from pulps which have not been
elemental chlorine bleached. This pulp is from farmed
sustainable forests and was produced with special regard
for the environment.
Throughout, the printing and binding have been planned
to ensure a sturdy, attractive publication which should
give years of enjoyment.
If your copy fails to meet our high standards,
please inform us and we will gladly replace it.*